DR. KEVIN LE[

RUNNING
THE RAPIDS

WORKBOOK

SAMPSON
RESOURCES

4887 Alpha, Suite 220 • Dallas, Texas 75244 • (972) 387-2806 • (800) 371-5248 • FAX 972-387-0150
www.sampsonresources.com   info@sampsonresources.com

HOW TO USE THIS WORKBOOK

The RUNNING THE RAPIDS workbook accompanies the six video lessons by Dr. Kevin Leman. The workbook is vital to the study because it helps make practical application of Dr. Leman's video lessons and is a reference to which you can refer for years to come. ***Use it aggressively!*** Whether you are completing the study with a group of couples or on your own, be sure to take notes on the video lessons and then work through the discussion guide, writing down your thoughts, ideas, and comments. Fill in every blank. **NOTE:** Each lesson — video and discussion — is designed to be completed in 55 to 60 minutes, but if you are unable to finish in the allotted time, feel free to continue it in the next session or complete the lessons on your own. May God bless you in your study of RUNNING THE RAPIDS.

TABLE OF CONTENTS

LESSON 1
KNOW THE RIVER. **4**
What's So Scary about Adolescence Anyway?

LESSON 2
KNOW THE RAFT **9**
Home Is Where You Transfer the Values That Teenagers Need
To Build a Positive Life

LESSON 3
KNOW THE RIDERS **15**
What Is Acceptable and Unacceptable Teenage Behavior and Why?

LESSON 4
KNOW THE RISKS. **21**
Tough Questions That Deserve Straight Answers

LESSON 5
KNOW THE RELATIONSHIPS **26**
Practical Guidelines for Surviving the Trip Together

LESSON 6
KNOW THE REALITY. **33**
You Don't Have To Navigate the River of Adolescence Alone Unless You
Choose To

LESSON 1

KNOW THE RIVER

What's So Scary about Adolescence Anyway?

SCRIPTURE

What is faith? It is the confident assurance that something we want is going to happen. It is the certainty that what we hope for is waiting for us, even though we cannot see it up ahead.

Hebrews 11:1

"You make a difference.
You are your child's best teacher."

Raising kids through their adolescent years is like guiding your family in a raft through whitewater rapids. The role of the guide on such a trip is vital. No one would want to take a whitewater trip without a capable guide. Because every parent has taken this trip before, parents can be encouraged because they know the journey already.

As parent and guide, you know the dangers that lie ahead for your teenager. You know the unseen, destructive forces that lie just below the surface. By trusting in God, by having faith in Him, you can find confident assurance amid turbulent waters.

Parents need to relay to their teenagers a sense of trust. Teens can trust their parents because parents have made this trip before and know the issues and challenges that teens face. Parents also need to know that they have much more influence on their kids' lives than they may realize. Sometimes parents sell themselves short and underestimate their influence, but the parental role is crucial and vital to a teen.

The adolescent years can be the best years in a family if parent and teen draw closer together and build an even stronger relationship of trust and encouragement. Your teenager does not want you to be a teenager. Your teen wants you to be the parent. Parents need to be firm yet understanding and encouraging as teens test their boundaries and search for significance.

Parents need to pay attention to three elements as they guide kids through adolescence. Parents need to . . .

1. **Decide to major on the majors, not on the minors**. Pick your battles. Not everything is worthy of concern and debate.

2. **Learn to say positive things to your child.** Children are a gift from God (Ps. 127:3). Make a special effort to affirm your kids when they make good choices.

3. **Find something their children can do well.** Emphasize this strength and help your teen feel accepted and special.

You are the key in your teenager's life. You may be scared about guiding the raft through turbulent waters, but you know the journey, and you can make a positive difference. Be a cheerleader for your child. Be on your child's team.

Key Thoughts from Video Lesson 1

"The more trips you take down the river, the more relaxed you can be."

1. The river is adolescence. It's scary to some and not to others.

2. As the parent, you are the helmsman. You are responsible for the cubs who come out of your den.

3. This is what has to connect you to your son or daughter: a sense of trust that you have been down this river before.

4. Don't sell yourself short. You have much more influence in your child's life than you may realize.

5. When does adolescence begin?
   Age ten for girls and age eleven for boys.

6. Three elements to pay attention to as you run the rapids:

   A. Major on the majors, not the minors.

   B. Learn to say positive things to your child.

   C. Find something your child can do well.

7. Be a cheerleader for your child.

DISCUSSION

1. One reason parents fear the adolescent years is that they remember the painful experiences from their own adolescence. Think about your teen years. In the space below, jot down a brief reminder of an adolescent experience that left an imprint on your life. Was that experience positive, negative, or both? Discuss it with others in your group.

_____

_____

_____

2. As a parent, your attitude toward adolescence will color how you guide your teenager through turbulent times. Read each of the following statements and check the responses that best describe your attitude toward your child's teenage years. Compare your responses to others in the group.

❏ I'm scared to death! Someone throw me a life preserver!

❏ It's no big deal. I'm not worried.

❏ I'm exhausted. I'm running on fumes.

❏ I'm excited, pumped, and ready for more.

❏ I'm overwhelmed. I don't know what to do next.

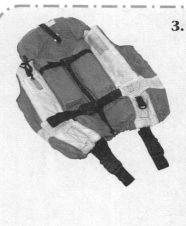

3. LIFESCENE: *Claire gave her parents ulcers when she was a teenager. An obedient child with lenient parents, Claire went wild as a teen and experimented with every taboo. Now that she's the parent of a teenage daughter, she does not want history to repeat itself. Claire drills her daughter, asking question after question, and is often skeptical of the answers she receives. She suspects that Angela is lying to her just as Claire lied to her parents. Claire decides to be anything but lenient and comes down hard on Angela, grounding her at every infraction of home rules. But the more Claire restricts and disciplines Angela, the more bizarre and disobedient Angela becomes. In spite of Claire's diligence and close monitoring of Angela, she fears that Angela is following in her footsteps.* Is this raft in jeopardy of hitting the rocks, or is this just a typical family with a teenager? What, if anything, do you think should be done? Discuss your response with others in the group.

_____

_____

_____

4. As helmsman of the family raft, a parent must decide how active and involved to be in his or her teenager's life. Some parents are too passive; some, too controlling. Rate your current level of involvement in your teen's life by placing an **X** on the following continuum. Then place a ✓ on the continuum to indicate the level of involvement you believe is needed.

Passive *Removed*						*Controlling* *Dictatorial*
1	2	3	4	5	6	7

5. Kids today are growing up too quickly. Television, movies, and peers influence your child's behavior, language, and dress. What signs in your teenager's world illustrate that kids are growing up too quickly? Discuss your insights with others in the group.

_____

_____

6. Dr. Leman encourages parents to talk to their teenagers about potential problems before they arise. But teens often are not interested in discussing matters that do not seem important to them. How can a parent find opportunities for such discussions?

_____

_____

7. Dr. Leman encourages parents to major on the majors, not on the minors. As you think about your home and your teenager, which issues are major, and which are minor? List your responses in the columns below.

Major Issues	**Minor Issues**
_____	_____
_____	_____
_____	_____
_____	_____

If you are married, complete #7 at home with your spouse. Agreeing in principle with your spouse on major and minor issues is important for a safe trip through the rapids of adolescence.

8. Psalm 127:3–5 states, *"Children are a gift from God; they are his reward. Children born to a young man are like sharp arrows to defend him. Happy is the man who has his quiver full of them. That man shall have the help he needs when arguing with his enemies."* What have you said to your teenager lately that expressed how much you cherish her or him?

_____

_____

_____

9. You may find it easy to be critical of and negative about your teenager. How can you avoid being a negative parent and instead genuinely and appropriately affirm your teen? Share your responses with others in the group.

_____

_____

_____

10. List some things your teenager does well. After completing your list, make a mental note to affirm your child in these areas.

_____

_____

_____

11. Based on the issues you have studied in this session, what changes do you think you need to make in relating to your teenager? Jot down your thoughts and share them with others.

_____

_____

_____

12. Join others in your group and pray for one another. Ask the Lord to guide you and other parents in being caring, loving, and involved guides as you steer your family through these critical years.

L E S S O N 2

KNOW THE RAFT

Home Is Where You Transfer the Values That Teenagers Need To Build a Positive Life

"The home makes all the difference in the world."

The raft represents your home and the things you do and don't do in your home. The home makes all the difference in the world. The home is where you transfer your values to your kids. Saying "Now hear this" is not the best method of communicating with your child.

Communication needs to be a regular event in your home, but communication is more than words. It's also actions. Our kids take notes on how we live our lives.

Start with the end in mind. What kind of young adult do you want to see emerge at the end of adolescence? Raise your child with that image in mind. The teenage years are crucial to raising a responsible, caring young adult.

The words we use at home make a major difference in how we move through turbulent times. The Bible says, *"Anyone who says he is a Christian but doesn't control his sharp tongue is just fooling himself, and his religion isn't worth much"* (James 1:26).

Remember that you cannot control your children just as God does not control us. God gives us freedom, but He also holds us accountable for our decisions. Give your teenager freedom but hold him or her accountable, too.

Kids need to feel a part of their family. Ask your child what he or she thinks, and seek input. Talk to them and listen to them. Build trust and teach trust to your child. You are a key person in your teenager's life.

SCRIPTURE

And you must think constantly about these commandments I am giving you today. You must teach them to your children and talk about them when you are at home or out for a walk; at bedtime and the first thing in the morning.
Deuteronomy 6:6–7

Blended families face turbulent times as they work to weave together different family histories and issues. If you are a single parent, be as consistent as possible. If you are able, stay single until your kids leave home.

Sometimes parents are too quick to bail their children out of trouble. Are you raising your child in a home or a hotel? Too often parents give their children everything they do not need. A judicious parent knows what a child truly needs and provides that.

Children need affirmation and a piece of the action. They need to be winners and to figure things out for themselves. They should be able to work and give back to the family and become better prepared for life. Allow your kids to pay the family bills or at least write the checks that pay the bills so they can understand the costs of raising a family.

Key Thoughts from Video Lesson 2

"You teach your values to your children by modeling. Values are caught, not taught."

1. Your raft represents your home.

2. Communication is more than words; it's also actions.

3. What part of the body did Dr. Leman refer to as the paddle or oar?

4. Parental poker is showing your hand, explaining your strategy to your kids.

5. Single parents: be as consistent as possible.

6. Are you raising kids in a home or a hotel?

7. Ask your child to pay or at least write the check for a family bill (e.g., utility, mortgage, grocery).

8. Create opportunities for your teenager to contribute to the family.

9. God uses ordinary people like you and me to touch and change people's lives.

10. Our kids are watching how we live our lives.

11. When you make a mistake, acknowledge it and apologize to your child or spouse.

DISCUSSION

1. Think about the home in which you grew up. What aspects of that home would you like to duplicate for your children? What aspects do you want to keep out of your children's lives? Jot down your thoughts, and discuss your ideas with others.

_____

_____

2. What values did you gain from your parents and grandparents? List these values in the left column below. In the right column, list some thoughts on how you can pass these values on to your children. Remember: values are *caught* more than they are *taught*.

Values I Learned from My Family	How I Can Pass These Values to My Kids
_____	_____
_____	_____
_____	_____
_____	_____
_____	_____

3. Read James 3:3–6:

We can make a large horse turn around and go wherever we want by means of a small bit in his mouth. And a tiny rudder makes a huge ship turn wherever the pilot wants it to go, even though the winds are strong. So also the tongue is a small thing, but what enormous damage it can do. A great forest can be set on fire by one tiny spark. And the tongue is a flame of fire. It is full of wickedness, and poisons every part of the body. And the tongue is set on fire by hell itself, and can turn our whole lives into a blazing flame of destruction and disaster.

What effect have words had on the state of your raft (home)? Jot down your thoughts, indicating both positive and negative influences your words have had.

_____

_____

4. LIFESCENE: *Trent is easygoing and laid back in nearly every area of his life. He prefers a hands-off approach to parenting. Trent's wife, Stephanie, is just the opposite. She borders on being obsessive-compulsive and is acutely focused on details and schedules. Trent and Stephanie have three children—ages six, nine, and eleven.* What problems or obstacles do you foresee for this family as you look down the river? Jot down your thoughts and discuss them with the group.

_____

_____

_____

What changes do you think are needed in Trent and Stephanie's home?

_____

_____

5. What kind of values are your children catching in your home? Values are *caught,* not *taught* as kids observe what their parents do. Place an X in the appropriate boxes below, indicating how often your children experience the following behaviors in your family.

Parental Behavior	Never	Seldom	Sometimes	Often
A parent loses his/her temper	❏	❏	❏	❏
A parent reads the Bible	❏	❏	❏	❏
A parent prays other than at mealtime	❏	❏	❏	❏
A parent uses profanity	❏	❏	❏	❏
A parent watches adult movies at home	❏	❏	❏	❏
A parent drinks alcoholic beverages	❏	❏	❏	❏
A parent uses a controlled substance	❏	❏	❏	❏
A parent attends worship in a church setting	❏	❏	❏	❏
A parent teaches a Bible class in a church	❏	❏	❏	❏
A parent uses sarcasm and ridicule	❏	❏	❏	❏
A parent says one thing but does another	❏	❏	❏	❏
A parent makes promises and then breaks them	❏	❏	❏	❏
A parent affirms and encourages the child(ren)	❏	❏	❏	❏
A parent spends quality time with each child	❏	❏	❏	❏
A parent shows love for his/her spouse	❏	❏	❏	❏

6. Begin with the end in mind. In what year will your child be 18?_____
(Write down the date.) Think about the character traits and values you want to see in your child's life by that time. List the three most important character traits or values in the left column below. In the right column, jot down a simple plan or action that could help you instill that quality or value in your child. **Remember:** values are *caught,* not *taught.*

Strengthening the Raft for _____(child's name)

Character Trait or Value My Child Needs	How I Can Instill This in My Child
_____	_____
_____	_____
_____	_____

7. Have you ever asked your teenager, "What do you think?" when considering a family vacation, a major purchase, or any other major or routine decision? Think of some situations or decisions when you could ask your teen for input. Write down your thoughts below. Discuss your ideas with the group.

_____

_____

8. How often do you bail out your teenager and keep him or her from facing the consequences of a poor decision? Write down a brief sentence describing the last such situation. If you could relive that situation, what would you do differently that would be better for your child?

_____

_____

9. Dr. Leman suggests giving kids "a piece of the action," assigning them work to do that will give back value to the family. What work, chores, or assignments is your child responsible for that help your child feel like a contributing, meaningful part of your family? Jot down these duties and discuss them with your group.

_____

_____

10. No parent is perfect. All of us make mistakes. Have you blown it recently with your teenager? If so, write down a few words that describe your most recent mistake.

_____

_____

11. Every home has problems, challenges, and struggles. Families are composed of imperfect people struggling to live, learn, and grow. First John 1:9–10 reminds parents that all of us sin. No parent is perfect. But when we confess our sins, Jesus will forgive us and purify us.

But if we confess our sins to him, he can be depended on to forgive us and to cleanse us from every wrong. And it is perfectly proper for God to do this for us because Christ died to wash away our sins. If we claim we have not sinned, we are lying and calling God a liar, for he says we have sinned.

12. Close this session by confessing your mistakes, failures, and sins to the Lord in prayer. Ask for His forgiveness. Then make an appointment with your teenager, and ask him or her to forgive you for the incident you described in #10.

LESSON 3

KNOW THE RIDERS

*What Is Acceptable and Unacceptable
Teenage Behavior and Why?*

"Be quick to listen to what's going on in your kid's life."

S C R I P T U R E

*Teach a child to choose
the right path, and
when he is older, he
will remain upon it.*

P r o v e r b s 2 2 : 6

Parents probably do not have a clue how bad life is for teenagers today. Kids are up against it. They face pressures we never faced growing up. Parents need to know what to expect from their teens during adolescence. What's normal behavior for a teenager today? There are perils ahead in your teenager's life, but there are calm times, too. Even in calm times there may be problems under the surface.

Parents need to adopt smart strategies and know their kids. Smart parents find ways to spend time with their teenagers, whether it's driving them to a sports event or a pottery class. The drive to and from such events offers opportunities for conversation and listening. Be quick to listen to what's going on in your child's life, and look for teachable moments.

Do not endure "smart mouth" comments from your teen. Parents can withhold a variety of privileges and freedoms to help curb sarcastic or disrespectful comments from teenagers.

Kids get hammered at school by derogatory nicknames and sarcasm from friends and peers. Try not to hammer your child or continually find fault. Instead, come alongside your teen and be an encouraging parent.

Respected psychologist Bruce Narramore describes *normal* negativity and *inappropriate* negativity during the teen years. Knowing when your teen's behavior crosses the line from normal to inappropriate is a judgment call.

Occasionally the parent will have to be the NFL referee and throw a flag, calling the teenager to account for crossing the line.

A child who feels close to his parents is less likely to engage in destructive behavior. By caring for and staying close to your child, you create a healthy shield around him/her. By your love, consistency, and involvement in your teenager's life, your child knows whether you are with him/her or not. Come alongside your child and discuss his/her problems. Throw out a life preserver and bring your teen on board.

There is something healthy about an unhappy teenager. Parents' goal is not to make their children happy all the time, nor is their goal to control their kids. Parents' goals should include loving and encouraging their kids and teaching them to be responsible and considerate of others.

Key Thoughts from Video Lesson 3

"Each child brings to life a variety of different experiences and needs."

1. We probably don't have a clue how bad it is out there today.

2. Kids are up against it. They face pressures today that we never faced.

3. Parents can curb "smart mouth" comments from their teenager.

4. Be quick to listen to what is going on in your child's life.

5. Kids get hammered at school by their peers. Don't hammer them all the time at home.

6. Dr. Bruce Narramore distinguishes between *normal* negativity and *inappropriate* negativity.

7. A child who feels close to his parents is less likely to engage in destructive behavior.

8. There's something healthy about an unhappy teenager.

DISCUSSION

1. In the many years since you entered adolescence, great changes have taken place in our world and your community. Your kids face issues and pressures today that are extremely complex and troubling. In what ways is being a teenager tougher today than when you were an adolescent? Write down your insights and discuss them with the group.

_____

_____

2. Of all the issues and temptations facing your teenager today, which ones give you the greatest concern and why?

_____

_____

3. Teenagers are not always ready to talk about their troubles and experiences when parents want to talk. Sometimes you have to just "be there" at the right moment and be a good listener. What is your secret to being a good listener and staying in touch with what is going on in your child's life? Write it down and discuss it with the group.

_____

_____

4. LIFESCENE: _John and Grace thought they were doing a good job raising their kids. Their firstborn, Taylor, has been the ideal child. She makes excellent grades in school, helps with chores at home, studies, and applies herself. Then along came their second child, Bradley. He loves video games, sports, and NASCAR. He seldom does his chores around the house, and his room is often a mess. Bradley hates school and hates to study. Sometimes John and Grace think he must have been adopted, but they know better! Everything John and Grace have done to encourage and motivate Bradley to be more like Taylor has been ineffective. They are at their wits' end._ What do you think would help John and Grace relate to Bradley? Write down your ideas and discuss them with the group.

_____

_____

_____

_____

5. Dr. Bruce Narramore, a well-known psychologist, contrasts the *normal* negativity expected in teenagers during adolescence with *inappropriate* negativity. Circle the words below that describe your teenager. Like the NFL referee, the parent has the difficult responsibility of determining when *normal* negativity approaches *inappropriate* negativity.

Normal Negativity	**Inappropriate Negativity**
Increased assertiveness	Chronic irritability
Direct expression of opinions and ideas	Chronic negativism
Increased forgetfulness	Rebellion
Complaining about chores	Defiance
Goofing off or being silly	Isolation
Making decisions that parents disagree with	Depression
Keeping secrets from parents	Raging outbursts
Occasional stubbornness	Prolonged, angry withdrawal
Periods of critical or condemning attitudes toward parents and other authority figures	

6. Dr. Leman advises parents not to be trigger-happy about marching their teenagers off to a counselor. He recommends throwing kids a life preserver —coming alongside them and discussing their problems with them. If you have tried coming alongside your teenager and discussing troubling issues, tell your group what you have learned about opening such dialogue. Do you find it easy or difficult to do? How do you initiate dialogue in a non-threatening way?

_____

_____

7. Dr. Leman says in the video lesson that there is something "healthy about an unhappy teenager." In other words, it is appropriate for teenagers to be unhappy at times. Do you agree or disagree? Complete one of the following statements, and be ready to share your response with the group.

❏ I agree because

_____

❏ I disagree because

_____

8. Remember Vitamin N (saying no to your teenager). Some parents have trouble giving their children this important vitamin. Why is saying no a challenge for some parents? Jot down your thoughts and discuss them with the group.

_____

_____

9. Here are some proverbs that refer to wisdom and teaching. How do these scriptures speak to your role as a parent? Read the scripture and then summarize the truth of the verse in the space to the right.

Listen to your father and mother. What you learn from them will stand you in good stead; it will gain you many honors. (Proverbs 1:8–9)

Just as a father punishes a son he delights in to make him better, so the Lord corrects you. (Proverbs 3:12)

But you—all you do is sleep. When will you wake up? "Let me sleep a little longer!" Sure, just a little more! And as you sleep, poverty creeps upon you like a robber and destroys you; want attacks you in full armor. (Proverbs 6:9–11)

Happy is the man with a level-headed son; sad the mother of a rebel. (Proverbs 10:1)

Some people like to make cutting remarks, but the words of the wise soothe and heal. (Proverbs 12:18)

If you refuse criticism, you will end in poverty and disgrace; if you accept criticism, you are on the road to fame. (Proverbs 13:18)

An old man's grandchildren are his crowning glory. A child's glory is his father. (Proverbs 17:6)

10. Facing the consequences of a poor decision is one of the best ways that teenagers learn and develop. Describe a recent situation in which you allowed your child to experience the consequences of a poor decision. Write a brief description of that event, and discuss it with the group.

_____

_____

11. Getting to know your teenager requires time—time that often comes at great personal expense. Are you willing to make the sacrifice of time to *really* get to know your son or daughter? What time can you clear in your schedule to spend with your teenager?

_____

_____

12. Based on what you have learned in this lesson about knowing the riders, what adjustments or changes do you need to make in your life to better guide your children through the turbulent waters of adolescence? Write down your ideas and discuss them with the group.

_____

_____

13. As you close this lesson, take time to pray with your group about what you have learned today. Ask the Lord to make you a better listener and a more loving parent. Include any other help that you need to be the parent your children need.

LESSON 4

KNOW THE RISKS

Tough Questions That Deserve Straight Answers

"Talk less. Say more."

SCRIPTURE

Discipline your son in his early years while there is hope. If you don't, you will ruin his life.

Proverbs 19:18

There are a lot of risks out there, and kids will discover life as it really is. When they do, you will have a variety of emotional responses. Be sure that you are in control of yourself and your feelings. At times you may need a twenty-four-hour cooling-off period before you address a problem in your child's life.

Have a frank talk with your child, and be right out in the open. Suppose you find a pornographic magazine in your son's bedroom. Rather than beginning with, "What a bad person you are!" consider saying, "I'm glad to see that you are interested in the opposite sex."

There is little consensus today among teens about what constitutes sex. What do you do when you learn that your teenage daughter is sexually active? Tell your child that her behavior is dangerous and wrong. Birth-control pills may protect her from pregnancy but not from sexually transmitted diseases (STDs). Do not be surprised if other parents are not alarmed by their children's sexual promiscuity. Fifty percent of today's high-school students have had sexual intercourse. By twelfth grade, the percentage is 60; by their twentieth birthday, the percentage is 80.

Too many parents today stick their heads in the sand and do not talk straight to their kids about sex. Parents must address these issues head-on. Do not hesitate to set boundaries and curfews for your kids. Talk less and say more. Actions speak louder than words.

Let your action make your child responsible for his/her behavior. Take tough action and be willing to endure your child's momentary anger. If you love your kids, you will discipline them.

Kids are ridiculed today for being virgins. They don't date anymore; they hang out. Your honest disclosure that you know what is happening in the world today goes a long way in helping protect your son or daughter.

If you need a method for talking to your child about sex, take him or her for a drive on an interstate highway. Then you can look out the window as you talk about sexual issues. Sometimes more can be accomplished in sex education by a father talking to his daughter and a mother talking to her son. A father can tell his daughter how guys think, and a mother can tell her son how young women want to be treated.

A prime indicator of how well a child will do in college is the value the parent places on higher education. Don't sell yourself short: you do make a difference.

Key Thoughts from Video Lesson 4

"If you love your kids, you will discipline them."

1. You find a pornographic magazine in your son's room. What do you do?

2. You discover that your daughter is sexually active. What do you do?

3. Teenagers are ridiculed today for being virgins.

4. Kids don't date anymore; they hang out.

5. Do you want to talk to your child about sex? Take him or her for a ride on the interstate.

6. The future for your child is Friday.

7. Don't tear your children down. Build them up.

8. A prime indicator of how well a child will do in college is the value the parent places on higher education.

9. If you cooperate with me, I'll cooperate with you.

10. Even though you may feel hopeless sometimes, you can make a difference in your child's life. Don't sell yourself short.

DISCUSSION

1. Think again about your teenage years. When you were going through adolescence, how did your parents help you understand and face the risks of those years? Jot down your memories and discuss them with the group.

_____

_____

2. Considering all that you know about your children, their friends, your community, and today's culture, what do you believe are the greatest risks facing your kids today?

_____

_____

3. LIFESCENE: _Connie is a single mother with two children: Kevin, age seventeen, and Courtney, age twelve. Connie depends on Kevin to pick up Courtney at school in the afternoon. While washing clothes, Connie discovered some drug paraphernalia in Kevin's jeans. When she confronted Kevin about the items, he shrugged it off, saying that everyone was experimenting with drugs, that it was no big deal. When Connie kept pressing Kevin to stay away from all drugs, he told her to back off, that he could handle it. Every time Connie brings up the subject, Kevin treats her as though she is unreasonable and is overreacting._ What, if anything, should Connie do? Write down your thoughts and discuss your ideas with the group.

_____

_____

_____

4. According to statistics, 50 percent of students in junior and senior high school have had sexual intercourse. What approach have you adopted, if any, to help your child save sex for marriage? Write down your plan or philosophy in the space below.

_____

_____

Discuss your approach with the group. Jot down any additional ideas or approaches that you discover through this dialogue.

_____

_____

5. Dr. Leman recommends that fathers talk to their daughters and mothers talk to their sons about sex. What do you think are the advantages and disadvantages of this approach?

_____

_____

6. When seeking cooperation from your kids or searching for disciplinary ideas for risky, unacceptable behavior, what privileges or freedoms can you control to gain your child's cooperation?

_____

_____

7. Sometimes parents who abused sex or drugs as teenagers are hesitant to confess their past behavior to their children. Do you think parents should openly discuss their failures with their children or keep such matters private? Explain your answer in the space below, and discuss this question with the group.

_____

_____

8. Try the following activity with your children this week. Write each "talking point" on a separate index card. On a sheet of paper, list these subjects in the order of importance you believe your teenager will give them (1 = most important, 10 = least important). Give the cards to your teen and ask him/her to read each subject and then arrange the cards in the order of importance to him/her. Next compare your list with your teenager's list. Invite your teenager to discuss these subjects with you at his or her convenience.

Talking Points

What clothes to wear and why	Getting into college
A reasonable curfew	Borrowing the family car
Understanding the opposite sex	Knowing how far is too far
Cell-phone privileges	(making out)
Part-time work and chores at home	When friends are cruel
Being a better student	

9. Dr. Leman recommends (1) cooling off before confronting a teenager's risky behavior, (2) having frank talks with your teenager—being right out in the open about the issues, (3) talking less and saying more, (4) taking tough action, (5) teaching boundaries to your child, and (6) helping your teenager see how his/her actions will influence him/her for years to come.

The writer of Proverbs understood the danger of sexual temptation and the risks involved for his sons. Read chapter 5, verses 1–15:

> *Listen to me, my son! I know what I am saying; listen! Watch yourself, lest you be indiscreet and betray some vital information. For the lips of a prostitute are as sweet as honey, and smooth flattery is her stock-in-trade. But afterwards only a bitter conscience is left to you, sharp as a double-edged sword. She leads you down to death and hell. For she does not know the path to life. She staggers down a crooked trail and doesn't even realize where it leads.*
>
> *Young men, listen to me, and never forget what I'm about to say: Run from her! Don't go near her house, lest you fall to her temptation and lose your honor, and give the remainder of your life to the cruel and merciless; lest strangers obtain your wealth, and you become a slave of foreigners. Lest afterwards you groan in anguish and in shame when syphilis consumes your body, and you say, "Oh, if only I had listened! If only I had not demanded my own way! Oh, why wouldn't I take advice? Why was I so stupid? For now I must face public disgrace."*
>
> *Drink from your own well, my son—be faithful and true to your wife.*

10. How many of Dr. Leman's six recommendations can you find in Proverbs 5:1–15? List your responses in the space below.

_____

_____

11. Review your notes from this lesson and your responses to the questions above. What issues or risks do you need to address with your teenager . . .

this week?

_____

this month?

_____

this year?

_____

12. Pray with others about the issues discussed in this lesson. Ask the Lord to open your eyes to the issues and risks facing your child. Also ask the Lord to give you wisdom and courage to speak to your child about these issues at the teachable moment.

L E S S O N

5

KNOW THE RELATIONSHIPS

Practical Guidelines for Surviving the Trip Together

S C R I P T U R E

And now a word to you parents. Don't keep on scolding and nagging your children, making them angry and resentful. Rather, bring them up with the loving discipline the Lord himself approves, with suggestions and godly advice.

E p h e s i a n s   6 : 4

"You cannot bring up teenagers today with just a set of rules."

Nearly everyone questions authority today, but teenagers need to understand the healthy imprint of authority. You are the authority in the home. Ephesians 6 teaches this truth. You cannot bring up teenagers today with just a set of rules. You need relationships.

Healthy teenagers exist on three pillars of understanding.

1. **They have to respect and obey their parents**. Have positive expectations for your children.
2. **They need to gain ownership of the belief that they are special people**. Have a special relationship with each of your kids.
3. **They should expect the best that life has to offer them**. Plant seeds in your child's life that give him or her things to look forward to in life.

Be open to your kids. Have open arms and an open mind. Follow through on what you say. Set realistic standards. Do not make life impossible. Give your child some slack when necessary.

Accept your child where he/she is. Don't keep bringing up your child's previous mistakes. Take time to listen to and respect your child's choices. Do not harangue or badger him/her. Respect your child's privacy.

If you love your child, you will discipline him/her. But never put your child in jail and throw away the key. Learn to use "reality discipline." Use every opportunity to teach and to mold your child's life.

Be honest with your teenager, and own up to your part of the relationship. Relationships in this raft (the home) are the most important in life. Neither sports nor school is more important than relationships in the home.

Use encouraging words: "Now you're getting it." "Nice job." "Looks like the extra practice is paying off." "These good grades must make you feel great."

Believe in your child. If you err, err on the side of believing your child.

Do not go to one extreme or the other. Stay inside the boundaries where God's love can reach you. Improve your relationship by questioning your child less and encouraging your child more.

Key Thoughts from Video Lesson 5

*"Be open to your kids.
Have open arms, an open mind."*

1. Teenagers need to know the healthy imprint of authority.

2. You are the authority in the home.

3. It's dangerous to overdo or underdo things.

4. Healthy teenagers exist on three pillars of understanding.

   A. They have to respect and obey their parents.

   B. They need to own the belief that they are special people.

   C. They should expect the best that life has to offer them.

5. Follow through on what you say. (Illustration of child who did not mow the lawn)

6. Set realistic standards. Don't make life impossible.

7. Accept your child where he or she is.

8. Take time to listen. God gave us two ears and one mouth.

9. Respect their choices. Allow kids to live with the consequences of their choices.

10. Respect your child's privacy.

DISCUSSION

1. When today's adults were growing up, it was common to have a good relationship with one parent and practically no relationship with the other. If this was true for you as an adolescent, why was your relationship poor or nonexistent with one parent? What was missing in that relationship that you needed? Write down your memories and discuss them with the group.

_____

_____

2. Is history repeating itself? Sometimes in spite of our best efforts, we may treat our kids the way we were treated—both for the good and the bad. If you are having a rocky relationship with one of your teenagers, do you see any similarities between that relationship and the poor relationship you had with one of your parents? Consider this for a moment and jot down your thoughts.

_____

_____

3. LIFESCENE: _Jill cringes every time she thinks about her teenage years. Her father was never home, and her mother was a strict disciplinarian who seldom allowed Jill time to breathe. As a teen, Jill rebelled against her parents in every way possible—morally, socially, and academically. If only she could erase the horrible memories of those years! Today she and her husband, Rob, are actively involved in their children's lives—from sports to school to friends. Their children seem to be normal teenagers, but Jill believes that their daughter Meredith is living a secret life. Jill doesn't trust Meredith and checks up on her frequently. She keeps Meredith on a short leash and frequently confronts her about her clothes, her friends, and her whereabouts. Their once-tranquil home is now a tense pressure cooker of anger and strife._ What do you think needs to be done to improve the relationships in this family? Jot down your thoughts and discuss them with the group.

_____

_____

_____

4. Ephesians chapters 5 and 6 provide guidance for parents and children on relationships in the home. Read the scriptures below. In the space to the right, summarize the truth of these verses in your own words.

Follow God's example in everything you do just as a much loved child imitates his father. Be full of love for others, following the example of Christ who loved you and gave himself to God as a sacrifice to take away your sins. (5:1–2a)

You wives must submit to your husbands' leadership in the same way you submit to the Lord. For a husband is in charge of his wife in the same way Christ is in charge of his body the church. (He gave his very life to take care of it and be its Savior!) So you wives must willingly obey your husbands in everything, just as the church obeys Christ. (5:22–24)

And you husbands, show the same kind of love to your wives as Christ showed to the church when he died for her . . . That is how husbands should treat their wives, loving them as parts of themselves. For since a man and his wife are now one, a man is really doing himself a favor and loving himself when he loves his wife! No one hates his own body but lovingly cares for it. (5:25, 28–29)

Children, obey your parents; this is the right thing to do because God has placed them in authority over you. Honor your father and mother. This is the first of God's Ten Commandments that ends with a promise. And this is the promise: that if you honor your father and mother, yours will be a long life, full of blessing. (6:1–3)

And now a word to you parents. Don't keep on scolding and nagging your children, making them angry and resentful. Rather, bring them up with the loving discipline the Lord himself approves, with suggestions and godly advice. (6:4)

5. One of the pillars of understanding for teens is respect for and obedience to parents. How can parents earn and keep this respect during these tumultuous years? Write down your thoughts and discuss them with the group.

_____

_____

6. What do you do with teenagers to convince them that they are special? What has worked for you in conveying this special identity to your children?

_____

_____

7. Being consistent is a challenge for parents. Sometimes we say one thing and do another. Or we warn and threaten and then fail to follow through. Check the statement that most closely describes your level of consistency in the home.

❏ I'm as consistent as they come. What I say is what I do.
❏ I am consistent, but I also consider each situation and adjust my response as necessary.
❏ Consistency is good, but I don't want to exasperate my kids.
❏ Sometimes I speak too quickly and then find I cannot back up what I say.

8. Parents often feel that teens make poor choices: clothing, diet, study habits, schedule, etc. Yet teenagers need to develop decision-making skills and learn to live with the consequences of their decisions. Think of a decision that your teenager made recently, a decision you questioned or knew was less than the best. How did you handle that situation? Did you allow your child to live with the consequences? Write down what happened, and share your experience with the group.

_____

_____

9. Dr. Leman describes "reality discipline" as a way of allowing children to experience the unpleasant consequences of unacceptable behavior and bad choices. Sometimes experiencing the consequences of a poor decision is a more powerful teacher than being punished for a bad decision. Consider how you would apply it in the following situations. In the right column, write a note describing how reality discipline could be applied in each situation.

Apply Reality Discipline

Your son got a second speeding ticket in two months.	
Your teen's grades are sliding as she tries to juggle an active social life, sports, and a part-time job.	
Your daughter was to pay for her prom dress by baby-sitting, but she turned down several baby-sitting invitations to spend time with friends. She needs more money.	

10. Integrity, love, and consistency in a parent are crucial in building a successful relationship with a teenager. In many families, parents are so busy with their own jobs and interests that they have little time for their kids. Take a moment to evaluate your contribution to your relationship with your teenager.

	Healthy	Adequate	Sporadic	Poor
Amount of time I spend with my teen	❏	❏	❏	❏
Encouragement and affirmation I give my teen	❏	❏	❏	❏
My ability to listen without criticizing and judging	❏	❏	❏	❏
My knowledge of my teen's friends and whereabouts	❏	❏	❏	❏
Communication with my teen's teachers	❏	❏	❏	❏
Example I set for my teen in church attendance	❏	❏	❏	❏
Opportunities I take to ask for forgiveness	❏	❏	❏	❏
My level of consistency in discipline and teaching	❏	❏	❏	❏
Honesty and truthfulness in all my relationships	❏	❏	❏	❏

11. Dr. Leman says that "believing your teenager" is important, and he uses the illustration from the Andy Griffith TV show. When a parent errs, it's good to err on the side of "believing your child." Do you agree or disagree? Explain your answer in the space below, and discuss this issue with the group.

_____

_____

12. Of all the subjects and ideas discussed in this lesson, which concepts and ideas are most important to you? Jot down these ideas and share them with the group.

_____

_____

13. Pray with others in your group, asking the Lord to give each parent wisdom and grace for building a healthy, loving relationship with his or her child.

LESSON 6

KNOW THE REALITY

You Don't Have To Navigate the River of Adolescence Alone Unless You Choose To

"You are the captain of the ship. You are the guide."

Adolescence is here, and it's not going away. Parents need to talk to their teens about potential problems before they arise. No one cares about your son or daughter the way you do. Don't let the "experts" run your life.

Invite your child's peer group to your house and pay for the pizza. Pick out a decent video or DVD. Let your child's friends discover you and your family. You will have the home-court advantage.

Believe in your kids and trust them until they prove untrustworthy. Pay special attention to changes in your child's behavior—abrupt or gradual. Find something your teen likes to do, and orchestrate a situation or event in which you and your teen can participate together. When a time opens up, talk to your teen about the change in his or her behavior. Be ready to listen. Keep your stance open.

Six ways to use peer pressure for your kid's benefit:

1. **Create a sense of belonging**. Help your child feel that he or she belongs in your family.
2. **Encourage close relationships**. Take time to get to know your child's friends.
3. **Get extraordinarily involved in the life of your kid**. Don't sell yourself short.

SCRIPTURE

There is a right time for everything:... A time to cry; A time to laugh; A time to grieve; A time to dance
Ecclesiastes 3:1, 4

4. **Select the environment in which your kids will grow up**. Where will your kids go to school? Will you homeschool?

5. **Provide stability**. We live in a mobile society, and sometimes we have to make difficult decisions. Live as close as you can to one set of grandparents so your kids will have contact with them.

6. **Become your child's excuse**. Sometimes your teenager does not want to go along with the crowd and needs your no as an excuse for backing out.

Your kids need a sense of realness from you. They love to hear about times in your life when you messed up, when you were less than perfect. They need to know that you are real and make mistakes too.

Go and do life well. Your kids are counting on you.

Key Thoughts from Video Lesson 6

"Kids need a sense of realness from you."

1. Invite your child's peer group to your home.

2. POS – Parent Over Shoulder

3. What do you do if your teenager starts to tune you out?

Six Ways to Use Peer Pressure for Your Kid's Benefit

A. Create a sense of belonging. Help your child feel that he belongs to your family.

B. Encourage close relationships.

C. Get involved in the life of your child.

D. Select the environment in which your child will grow up.

E. Provide stability. What about that promotion that would force your family to move?

F. Become your child's excuse. (Illustration of wanting the car to go to IHOP.)

DISCUSSION

1. Having already gone through adolescence, parents recognize the dangers along the river and the hope that's waiting at the end. Having "been there," how can you use your experience to provide hope and assurance to your teenager that he or she can make it successfully?

_____

_____

2. Dr. Leman encourages parents to orchestrate situations and events so they can spend time with their teenagers. Such occasions provide opportunities to listen, to learn, and to build rapport. Think about your schedule this week. How can you orchestrate some time with your teenager to get reacquainted? Jot down ideas and discuss them with the group.

_____

_____

3. One way to use peer pressure for your child's benefit is to create a sense of belonging. When teens feel they belong to the family, they are less likely to drift into groups that will exert negative influences. How can parents help their teens feel connected and needed in the family and still allow their kids freedom to be with other teenagers away from the family? Write down some ideas and discuss them with the group.

_____

_____

4. LIFESCENE: _Rachel believes that she is always saying no to her son Caleb. Almost every day Caleb asks to go somewhere with his friends or to do something that Rachel believes is not suitable or good for him. Caleb is beginning to develop a negative relationship with his mother and accuses her of trying to keep him from having a normal life and enjoying his friends. Hardly a week goes by without an angry exchange or standoff. The distance between Rachel and her son seems to grow daily. Rachel does not want to give in to Caleb just to keep the peace, but she also does not want to lose him altogether._ What do you recommend to help Rachel and Caleb create and maintain a close relationship? Write down your thoughts and discuss them with the group.

_____

_____

_____

5. Dr. Leman says that parents can encourage close relationships for their teenagers by orchestrating their children's friendships. How can parents orchestrate friendships for their teens without appearing controlling and dictatorial?

_____

_____

6. How can parents learn more about their teenagers' friends? How can parents discover whether someone is the kind of person who would be good for their child? Write down your ideas and discuss them with the group.

_____

_____

7. How can parents be involved in the lives of their teenagers without becoming their children's shadow or 24/7 bodyguard? What are some positive ways to be involved in your child's life? Discuss your ideas with the group.

_____

_____

8. Providing stability in their children's lives is a crucial gift parents can give their kids. But stability comes at great personal sacrifice and demands wisdom and discernment on the part of parents. Meet with your group and discuss the following questions. In the right column below, list various issues that need to be addressed when considering the opportunities noted in the left column. How do these opportunities bring both blessing and chaos to a family?

Opportunity	Issues to be Addressed
Teenage son wants to try out for a competitive sports team	
Mom wants to work part-time to help make extra money for the family	
Daughter wants to work after school to earn money for a car	
Dad receives a major promotion that will require his traveling more	
The family receives a large inheritance from a relative	

9. Dr. Leman recommends that parents at times become their child's "excuse." Perhaps your teenager does not want to go along with the crowd and needs your no as an excuse for backing out. Being your child's "excuse" can be an unpopular, lonely role, especially when other parents seem more lenient or permissive. If you have been your child's excuse, how did you feel about that role? Jot down some real-life situations and discuss them with your group.

_____

_____

10. Driving skills, car insurance, money for gas, and other important issues surround your teenager's experience in driving an automobile. Discuss with your group the following questions, and jot down some notes in the space to the right.

When can a teenager get a driver's license?

_____

Who pays for car insurance?

_____

Who pays for gas and car maintenance?

_____

What happens when a teenager has an accident or gets a speeding ticket?

_____

What responsibilities accompany the privilege of driving a car?

_____

Should parents require their child to take driver's education training?

REVIEW

11. Take a moment to review all six lessons in this workbook. In the space to the right of each lesson title, jot down one main idea from that lesson.

1. Know the River _____

2. Know the Raft _____

3. Know the Riders _____

4. Know the Risks _____

5. Know the Relationships _____

6. Know the Reality_____

12. Congratulations on completing these six practical lessons on "guiding teenagers through the turbulent waters of adolescence." Think about all of the ideas, insights, and inspiration you have gained through this study. Read the following statement and complete it according to what you plan to add to your raft.

Having experienced and survived adolescence myself and knowing and loving my child as I do, I want to help my teenager run the rapids with joy and assurance and enter adulthood with a sense of confidence and optimism. As a parent committed to honoring the Lord, I commit to guide my teenager by . . .

_____   _____
Signature   today's date

13. Complete this study by praying with the group. Pray specifically for each parent and for the members of each family. Ask the Lord to guide you and give you wisdom, grace, and love for the journey ahead.

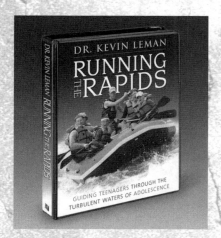

Not Your Typical Family Expert
The latest from Dr. Kevin Leman

First-Time Mom
ISBN 0-8423-6039-5
$13.99

First-time parents learn about ways to raise a happy, healthy first born child.

Running the Rapids
ISBN 0-8423-7413-2
$13.99

Strap on your life preserver and join Dr. Leman as he guides you through the turbulent waters of adolescence.

Home Court Advantage
ISBN 1-58997-207-4
$22.99

Home Court Advantage points to a richer philosophy of parenting and gives practical pointers on how to achieve it.

Sheet Music
ISBN 0-8423-6024-7
$12.99

Dr. Leman offers a practical guide to sex according to God's plan.

"There are only two kinds of families,
those who are working to get better
& those who better get working."

Dr. Kevin Leman